# Mr. Tash

**'Mr Tash'**
An original concept by Yasmin Finch
© Yasmin Finch

Illustrated by Abigail Tompkins

**Published by MAVERICK ARTS PUBLISHING LTD**
Studio 3A, City Business Centre, 6 Brighton Road,
Horsham, West Sussex, RH13 5BB
© Maverick Arts Publishing Limited November 2018
+44 (0)1403 256941

A CIP catalogue record for this book is available at the British Library.

**ISBN 978-1-84886-388-0**

*Maverick*
publishing
www.maverickbooks.co.uk

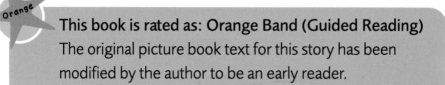

Orange

This book is rated as: Orange Band (Guided Reading)
The original picture book text for this story has been
modified by the author to be an early reader.

# Mr. Tash

by **Yasmin Finch**

illustrated by **Abigail Tompkins**

Mr Tash is very, very tall, and very, very thin.

He has a very, very long coat...

...and very, very shiny black boots.

4

"It's a fantabulous day for a picnic!"

he thinks.

Mr Tash marches down the street.
His extra-long, super-duper, curly-wurly
moustache flies in the wind.

Tall children have to duck under it.

Small children try to snatch at it.

Birds like to nest in it.

Mr Tash enjoys his picnic, but then

he spies the roundabout.

"Oh! A roundabout," he says.

He runs over, and gives the
roundabout a little push.

Mr Tash hops on. "Perfect!"

He whirls round and round and faster and round

and faster and round and round and ROUND!

Oh no...

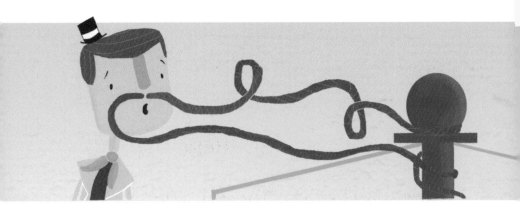

Mr Tash's extra long, super-duper,
curly-wurly moustache...

...whirls round and round
the roundabout's middle.

"Aghhhh!" he shouts, "Help! HELP!"

He twists. He tugs. But Mr Tash is
STUCK.

One super strong girl tries pulling.

Mr Tash stays stuck.

Two clever boys try slippery soap.

Mr Tash stays stuck.

Three wise grannies try to help too.

Mr Tash stays stuck.

"This is not fantabulous," he says.

Nine big builders try to shake him off,

but it's no good.

So one of the ten tall teachers has to snip Mr Tash's moustache off.

At last he is free.

The next morning, Mr Tash looks in the mirror. This will not do.

Mr Tash must have a moustache.

He thinks hard.

Two old toothbrushes? NO.

Two little mice? NO.

Two fluffy feathers? NO.

Two stripey socks...?

# Perf

e c t !

Mr Tash marches down the street.

His extra-long, super-duper, stripey-

wipey sock moustache flies in the wind.

"What a super new moustache!"

he thinks. "Tomorrow I think I'd like...

a banana one."

# Quiz

1. What does Mr Tash decide to do?
a) Go to the zoo
b) Have a picnic
c) Go shopping

2. Who likes to nest in Mr Tash's moustache?
a) Birds
b) Ants
c) Socks

3. Why does Mr Tash's moustache become tangled?
a) Because he plays with soap
b) Because he does not brush it
c) Because he plays on the roundabout

4. How does Mr Tash get free?
a) A strong girl pulls him free
b) A teacher cuts his moustache
c) A granny untangles him

5. What makes a perfect, new moustache?
a) Two little mice
b) Two fluffy feathers
c) Two stripey socks

*Turn over for answers*

# Book Bands for Guided Reading

The Institute of Education book banding system is a scale of colours that reflects the various levels of reading difficulty. The bands are assigned by taking into account the content, the language style, the layout and phonics. Word, phrase and sentence level work is also taken into consideration.

Maverick Early Readers are a bright, attractive range of books covering the pink to white bands. All of these books have been book banded for guided reading to the industry standard and edited by a leading educational consultant.

Pink

Red

Yellow

Blue

Green

Orange

Turquoise

Purple

Gold

White

To view the whole Maverick Readers scheme, visit our website at

www.maverickearlyreaders.com

Or scan the QR code above to view our scheme instantly!

*Quiz Answers: 1b, 2a, 3c, 4b, 5c*